Chuck Austen
Writer

Ivan Reis
Penciller

Marc Campos
Inker

**Joe Prado &
Jon Sibal**
Additional art

Guy Major
Colorist

Comicraft
Letterer

Art Adams
Original covers

Superman created by
Jerry Siegel &
Joe Shuster

SUPERMAN: THE WRATH OF GOG

"YOU SAW HE WAS UPSET AND DID THE SWEETEST THING. RIGHT OUT OF NOWHERE.

"I'D NEVER SEEN YOU BEFORE BUT I FELL IN LOVE WITH YOU THAT VERY INSTANT."

AND I THINK CLARK DID, TOO. EVEN THEN, I ALWAYS IMAGINED YOU TWO WOULD...

WOULD WHAT? END UP MARRIED?

I DON'T KNOW. IT WAS A SILLY NOTION. BUT YOU KIDS GREW UP TOGETHER AND--

WELL, IT'S NOT LIKE I DIDN'T HAVE MY CHANCE.

I DON'T KNOW, I HAD A LOT OF CRAZINESS TO GET OUT OF MY SYSTEM, WHAT WITH THE BAD MEMORIES OF LOSING MY PARENTS HERE, AND YEARS OF LIVING IN FOSTER CARE. AND EVEN THOUGH CLARK ALWAYS *TALKED* ABOUT LEAVING SMALLVILLE, I NEVER BELIEVED HE ACTUALLY WOULD.

I WAS *AFRAID* HE NEVER ACTUALLY WOULD, AND THAT HE'D KEEP ME HERE WITH HIM. HE LOVES YOU AND MR. KENT SO.

HE LOVES THIS TOWN AND THIS FARM--

NOW THAT I'VE BEEN AWAY, I FINALLY UNDERSTAND WHY. I WISH I COULD GO BACK AND DO THINGS DIFFERENTLY.

I'M SORRY THINGS DIDN'T WORK OUT BETTER WITH PETE. DO YOU THINK YOU'LL MOVE BACK? NOW THAT YOU TWO ARE GETTING A DIVORCE?

I CAN'T. I'D LIKE TO. IT'S SO MUCH MORE PEACEFUL HERE, AFTER ALL I'VE GONE THROUGH WITH PETE, AND NOW HIS DECISION TO--

I DON'T KNOW. THE ONLY WORK I COULD GET WAS IN METROPOLIS, ANYWAY.

SO AT LEAST YOU'LL BE NEAR CLARK AGAIN.

I'M SORRY. I DIDN'T THINK THAT WOULD BE A SORE SUBJECT.

YOU'LL FIND SOMEONE ELSE.

I HOPE SO. NOT MANY MEN WANT TO TAKE ON A WOMAN WITH A CHILD BY ANOTHER MAN.

HOW WAS IT FOR YOU, MR. KENT? RAISING SOMEONE ELSE'S BABY AS YOUR OWN?

AMAZING.

IT'S NOT THE KIND OF THING I WOULD HAVE SET OUT TO DO ON PURPOSE, BUT THE EXPERIENCE WAS SOMETHING I WOULDN'T HAVE TRADED FOR THE WORLD. CLARK WAS A GIFT TO ME. AN INCREDIBLE BOY. HOW COULD I NOT LOVE HIM WITH ALL MY HEART? WHATEVER GENES HE HAD.

OF COURSE, CLARKIE HAS A FATHER, WHICH IS DIFFERENT THAN WHAT WE EXPERIENCED. JONATHAN NEVER HAD TO COMPETE WITH CLARK'S NATURAL DAD.

IT'S FUNNY THAT YOU USE THE WORD COMPETE. I THINK PETE ALWAYS SAW IT THAT WAY.

"AS A COMPETITION."

"A COMPETITION HE LOST."

THE STORY THUS FAR...

Faster than a speeding bullet, more powerful than a locomotive, able to leap the tallest buildings with a single bound...**Superman** is known to all as the world's greatest super-hero. While he has faced many challenges that have tested his heroic abilities, the Man of Steel now finds himself in a situation that has its roots in several of his past adventures...

Although he is a protector of all mankind, Superman calls **Metropolis** home. A sprawling city teeming with skyscrapers and bustling with activity, Metropolis is known to many as the City of Tomorrow.

Superman found himself manipulated by the enigmatic **Futuresmiths**, cloaked beings who used Metropolis's futuristic technology to change the course of time. In an effort to confuse and distract the Man of Steel from their true plans, they engineered many events, including the creation of **Cir-El** — a new Supergirl who claimed to be Superman's daughter — and a robotic Superman from a far-flung future who warned of an impending technological doom thanks to the Futuresmiths.

Clark Kent and his *Daily Planet* editor Perry White faked Kent's firing, allowing him to go undercover to look for proof that President Lex Luthor was engaged in criminal activities. Shortly thereafter, Superman and Batman began an assault on Luthor to bring him down once and for all. Luthor, in turn, once more tried to turn the populace against its otherworldly protector by proclaiming a meteor approaching Earth was from Krypton and could wipe out humanity. The heroes prevailed, bringing down the president. Vice President Pete Ross was sworn in as president to complete the term.

Perry rehired Clark to return to the *Planet*, but in a lesser role. Before Clark could reestablish himself, Metropolis was thrust into a new crisis.

The **Robot Superman** took Kal-El into the time stream itself to witness how his actions in the present were all planned to bring about the Futuresmiths and unleash a deadly nanotech virus upon humankind. Finally, thousands of years in the future, Superman confronted the Futuresmiths, who were revealed to be merely servants of another consciousness: Brainiac 12. This iteration of the green-skinned despot used Cir-El to take hold in the present (disguised as the one thing Superman would not attack: his offspring) and ensure a world overrun by machines that would give rise to an even more powerful Brainiac 13. Locked in a struggle with Brainiac 12, Superman was knocked into the time stream, where he left his foe trapped inside a temporal anomaly, imprisoned in a sort of phantom zone. This act of heroism left Superman adrift through time, tumbling through a multitude of possible realities until he found his way home.

With Superman gone, Earth was troubled. A hero from another reality, Majestic, briefly helped out, seeing to it that time corrected itself and Metropolis was returned to its normal 21st-century splendor. Superman's friends and especially his wife, Lois, felt adrift. His return signaled a fresh start.

Almost immediately upon the restoration of the time stream, the asteroid crashed into the ocean and brought with it Kal-El's cousin Kara. Over a period of weeks, she acclimated herself to Earth, currently training with the Amazons on Themyscira.

Meantime, life continued as White hired Jack Ryder to fill Kent's investigative reporting slot. When Clark Kent was finally ready to return to work, he had to settle for something lower on the food chain.

Accounts of these events can be found in the following collections:

I CAN'T REALLY DO ANYTHING UNTIL PERRY GIVES ME AN ASSIGNMENT.

USUALLY HE'LL SEE ME *WHENEVER* I STOP BY.

IT'S JUST A REALLY BUSY DAY TODAY, CLARK.

ANOTHER HOUR. PROMISE.

WANNA GRAB SOME DINNER OVER AT BIBBO'S?

BOOOM

I THOUGHT I MADE IT **VERY CLEAR** TO YOUR MASTER, KALIBAK--

--STAY OUT OF MY CITY!

CHOOM

YOU **DIE** FOR THAT!

PROMISES, PROMISES.

CHUNK

STEPPENWOLF? HELLO? INDESTRUCTIBLE?

WHAM

IT'S IN THE NAME. SUPER--

--MAN.

THROOM

GET IT?

"SUPER," AS IN "I AM BETTER THAN YOU ARE."

CRRRUUNCH

AND "MAN," AS IN STAY -- OFF -- MY--

CHOOM

LOIS TO SEE YOU, PERRY.

OH, HI LOIS. COME ON IN.

YOU HAVEN'T TOLD MY HUSBAND THAT YOU'VE DEMOTED HIM, YET, HAVE YOU, PERRY?

IT WAS AN INSANE DAY. I'LL TALK TO HIM TOMORROW. OKAY?

BUT PERRY, I CAN'T KEEP SOMETHING LIKE THIS FROM CLARK! HE'S **MY HUSBAND!**

HALF THE **STAFF** KNOWS. HE'S **BOUND** TO FIND OUT--

HE WON'T FIND OUT. I **SWEAR** TO YOU. NO ONE WILL SAY ANYTHING. THEY KNOW IT NEEDS TO COME FROM ME.

AND I'D STILL APPRECIATE IT IF YOU LET IT...

"...SO PLEASE DON'T SAY ANYTHING, LOIS. PLEASE."

HI, SWEETIE. IT'S ME.

HEY, STRANGER. I'VE MISSED YOU. DIDN'T SEE YOU ALL DAY.

YOU'LL BE HOME FOR DINNER? I'M COOKING SOME --

I CAN'T, HONEY. I'M SORRY. I HAVE TO FINISH A STORY AND CONVINCE PERRY THAT I'M THE ONE TO COVER THE COALITION ACTION IN UMEC.

BREAKFAST TOMORROW. I PROMISE.

SURE. I UNDERSTAND.

SO, HOW WAS YOUR DAY? ANYTHING INTERESTING HAPPEN?

...

NO. NO, NOT REALLY.

AND YOU? WHAT DID YOU DO TODAY?

OH, YOU KNOW, NOTHING SPECIAL.

JUST ANOTHER DAY AT THE OFFICE.

I THINK I HAVE A RIGHT TO BE UPSET, LOIS. YOU KNEW I WAS GETTING DEMOTED TO THE SHACK AND YOU DIDN'T TELL ME.

IF I CAN'T TRUST MY WIFE TO TELL ME THESE THINGS, THEN WHO CAN I TRUST?

CLARK, THAT'S NOT FAIR. YOU CAN TRUST ME, OKAY? I NEVER MEANT TO HURT YOU, AND I'M SORRY.

I GUESS PART OF ME CAN'T EVEN BELIEVE YOU'RE UPSET. YOU'RE SUPERMAN, FOR GOD'S SAKE.

WHEN DID YOU KNOW, LOIS?

CLARK, I'M SORRY, ALL RIGHT? I'M REALLY, REALLY SORRY. IT WASN'T A CONSPIRACY, IT JUST CAME UP IN AN EDITORIAL MEETING.

BILL LOVING MENTIONED YOUR REPLACEMENT AND I GOT SUSPICIOUS AND CALLED THEM ON IT.

THEY HAD BEEN KEEPING IT FROM ME TOO, YOU KNOW?

PERRY TOLD ME TO PLEASE KEEP IT QUIET--HE WAS GOING TO SPEAK TO YOU RIGHT AFTER THAT MEETING--AND THEN TWO WEEKS LATER, HE STILL HADN'T, AND--

TWO WEEKS?

LOIS, YOU KNEW ABOUT THIS FOR TWO WEEKS AND YOU DIDN'T TELL ME?

CLARK, I'VE BEEN BUSY. I'M GETTING READY FOR THIS MIDDLE EAST TRIP--

--I'M SUPPOSED TO BE IN AN INTERVIEW NOW--

--YOU'VE BEEN BUSY--OFF SAVING THE WORLD EVERY TWO MINUTES, SO DON'T--

DON'T START THAT, OKAY? DON'T MAKE THIS MY FAULT. I'M HAVING A REALLY BAD WEEK HERE, DEMOTED BECAUSE I "NO LONGER APPEAL TO A YOUNGER DEMOGRAPHIC"--

--AND THE ONLY THING THAT COULD MAKE THIS WORSE IS IF I GOT REPLACED BY THAT SLIMEBALL JACK RYDER--

--AND THAT RUMOR IS GOING AROUND, YOU KNOW.

IS IT HIM, LOIS? IS IT RYDER?

...

CLARK? PLEASE. I'M SO, SO SORRY, AND I DON'T WANT TO FIGHT, OKAY?

I'M TIRED AND I REALIZE NOW HOW UPSETTING THIS IS TO YOU, BUT WE HAVE TO TALK LATER, OKAY?

EXCUSE ME, CLARK?

NAME'S JACK RYDER. OTHERWISE KNOWN AS "SLIMEBALL." JUST WANTED TO STOP BY AND SAY "THANKS" FOR VACATING YOUR JOB.

CLARK?

CLARK, ARE YOU THERE?

CLARK, CAN YOU HEAR ME?

IS EVERYTHING OKAY?

WELL.

I GUESS I CAN UNDERSTAND YOU BEING A LITTLE BITTER.

AND THAT'S PART OF THE REASON I TOOK THE JOB.

OH, AND TRY TO BE OUT OF THE OFFICE BY LUNCH, OKAY? EVEN THOUGH I'M KEEPING THE STUDIO OFFICE FOR MY HIGHLY LUCRATIVE TELEVISION CAREER, I *WILL* BE SPENDING *SOME* TIME HERE, SO I HAVE WORKMEN BRINGING A FEW THINGS OVER--

--AND I'D REALLY HATE FOR THEM TO BE TRIPPING OVER YOU.

CLARK!

SUPERMAN?

SUPERMAN, IT'S SUPERBOY. DOOMSDAY'S NOT--

CLARK?!

SUPERBOY?

CLARK? WHO ARE YOU TALKING TO?

ARE YOU ALL RIGHT?

CLAAAAARK!

SSZZZZZCRAKK

NNNNN...

WHO--
WHO ARE YOU?

TELL ME... OR TELL HIM.

--YESTERDAY!

ALL THE PEOPLE ARE SAFE, SUPERMAN.

THIS IS A *WICKED* FIGHT! SUPERMAN JUST POUNDED THAT DUDE!

NO RUBBER-NECKING! GET TO SAFETY!

AND PERRY SAYS I CAN'T APPEAL TO A YOUNGER DEMOGRAPHIC.

HA!

YOU AND ALL YOUR PROGENY, SUPERMAN--

--YOU WILL ALL DIE HORRIBLY, I PROMISE YOU.

-- BEHIND US AGAIN?

I'VE TRIPLE-CHECKED AND WE DEFINITELY GOT EVERYONE TO SAFETY.

WHAT *NOW?*

SUPERMAN SAYS TO GET *OURSELVES* TO SAFETY, BUT --

-- I DON'T KNOW, DON'T YOU THINK WE SHOULD BE HELPING THEM WITH --

CHOOOM

WHO IS THIS GUY?

YOU ALL RIGHT?

MMM, NOT REALLY, NO.

YEAH, YOU DON'T LOOK SO GOOD. LET'S GET YOU TO A DOCTOR OR SOMETHING.

CAN'T DO IT.

HE'LL BE BACK, AND I'VE GOTTA STOP HIM BEFORE HE HURTS SOMEONE.

SOMEONE BESIDES ME, THAT IS.

YOU THREE GO GET HELP, IN CASE I CAN'T DO THIS ALONE. THE JLA, MORE TITANS --

WHAT'S THAT GREEN STUFF HE INJECTED INTO YOU?

KRYPTONITE, I THINK.

LIQUEFIED.

OH MY GOD!

KAKOOOM

SUPERMAN?

SUPERMAN?!

SUPERMAN, ARE YOU --

CHRUNK

OH, NO.

FZZSSH

SOME OF THE SURVIVORS SAID CLA --

-- I MEAN SUPERMAN WAS TAKEN AWAY UNCONSCIOUS, BUT NO ONE WILL TELL US ANYTHING.

I CAN'T REACH LOIS, AND I'M REALLY SCARED, LANA. HAVE YOU HEARD ANYTHING?

NO, BUT WE'LL FIND OUT WHAT HAPPENED TO HIM, I PROMISE. AND I'M SURE HE'S FINE.

I KNOW HE WAS KILLED ONCE BEFORE, AND I CERTAINLY DON'T DOUBT IT COULD HAPPEN AGAIN, I JUST --

HE'S SUPERMAN, YOU KNOW. IT'S NOT THE EASIEST THING IN THE WORLD TO --

SUPERMAN IS DEAD.

OR HE MAY NEARLY BE SO, INJECTED WITH SOME FORM OF POISON, AND BEATEN SENSELESS BY A RANDOM VILLAIN.

I'M JACK RYDER FOR CHANNEL 6 NEWS HERE IN FRONT OF S.T.A.R. LABS -- -- WHERE MOMENTS AGO SUPERMAN'S APPARENTLY LIFELESS BODY WAS BROUGHT IN BY THE YOUNG HERO CALLING HIMSELF "SUPERBOY."

AS SOON AS WE HAVE ANSWERS FROM INSIDE, I WILL WAVE A BLUE FLAG FOR ALIVE, GREEN FOR INJURED, OR RED FOR DEAD.

LORD KNOWS HE COULD BE DEAD ONE MINUTE AND ALIVE THE NEXT -- IT'S HAPPENED BEFORE --

BUT FOR NOW, EARLY SOURCES INDICATE THAT THE HERO OF METROPOLIS KNOWN TO ONE AND ALL AS SUPERMAN --

MOHLMAN? ARE YOU IN CHARGE HERE? IS THERE SOMEONE *ELSE* WHO MIGHT BE ABLE TO HELP US -- *ANYONE* ELSE?

ISN'T IT PAST YOUR BEDTIME, MOHLMAN? WHERE'S FAULKNER, OR CHARLES, OR --

I DON'T KNOW. WHAT DO YOU NEED THEM FOR? I CAN HANDLE THIS.

I GOT PROMOTED. WELL, NOT EXACTLY PROMOTED, BUT I'D BEEN THREATENING TO QUIT, AND I WAS ON CALL, SO --

WHAT WAS THAT STUFF THAT WAS INJECTED INTO ME? WAS IT KRYPTONITE?

LIQUEFIED, YES.

FAAAAA-SCINATING, ACTUALLY. EARLY TESTS SHOW AN ORDERLY MOLECULAR STRUCTURE INDICATING A POTENTIAL *SYNTHETIC* ORIGIN.

IT HAS BASE NUCLEOTIDES, THOUGH, WHICH MEANS --

MOHLMAN. WHAT'S IT *DONE* TO ME?

OH MY *GOD!* IT'S ENABLED US TO LOOK *INSIDE* YOU.

X-RAY, BLOOD WORK, TISSUE SAMPLES --

-- WHICH I KNOW OTHERS HAVE DONE BEFORE BUT THEY WOULDN'T LET ME INTO THE ROOM, FOR SOME REASON.

AND I HAVE TO ADMIT, IT WAS A LITTLE *BORING*, ACTUALLY. TOTALLY ANTI-CLIMACTIC.

I HAD HOPED FOR SOMETHING MORE *ALIEN*, YOU KNOW? LIKE MIDICHLORIANS.

BUT -- -- AND THIS IS, LIKE, SOOO HUGE -- DID YOU KNOW YOUR **APPENDIX** IS A FULLY FORMED **ORGAN?**

I, FOR ONE, THINK WE SHOULD REMOVE IT AND DO SOME **SERIOUS** ANALYSIS, SO IF YOU'LL CONSENT TO AN OPERATION --

MOHLMAN.

-- IT WOULD BE MINIMALLY INVASIVE --

MOHLMAN.

IT WOULD TAKE FIVE MINUTES. AN HOUR TOPS.

MOHLMAN. I MEANT -- -- HOW HAS IT AFFECTED **ME?** ME **PERSONALLY.** ME **PHYSICALLY.**

MY STRENGTH? MY POWERS? MY INVULNERABILITY?

MY **LIFE,** MOHLMAN? IS MY **LIFE** IN **DANGER** WITH THIS STUFF COURSING THROUGH ME?

WELL, YOU WERE **DEAD** UNTIL JUST A MINUTE AGO.

AND -- -- HOW AM I **NOW?**

HOW SHOULD I KNOW?

WE COULD DO MORE TESTS, I SUPPOSE.

BUT WHO UNDERSTANDS YOUR PHYSIOLOGY WELL ENOUGH TO KNOW WHAT'S NORMAL?

YOUR RESTING HEART RATE IS NEAR STOPPED. YOUR BODY TEMPERATURE SLIGHTLY ELEVATED. BLOOD PRESSURE NEXT TO NOTHING.

IS THAT GOOD? BAD? I DON'T KNOW.

DO YOU?

NO. NO. I HAVE NO IDEA.

WE'VE NEVER REALLY BEEN ABLE TO DO EXTENSIVE TESTS ON MY PHYSIOLOGY BEFORE. IT COULD BE FINE, OR --

-- OR IT COULD BE TOTALLY BAD. YEAH.

IF I WERE YOU, I'D GO SPEND THE NEXT SEVERAL DAYS WITH SOME FAMILY -- OR -- YOU KNOW -- ONLINE FRIENDS.

SAY GOODBYE -- STUFF LIKE THAT. JUST IN CASE.

AWESOME BEDSIDE MANNER, DUDE.

I **DON'T** DO DEAD.

EXCELLENT.

TOTALLY EXCELLENT.

NOW, HOW ABOUT WE LOOK AT THAT APPENDIX OF YOURS?

WE HAVE SOMETHING FAR MORE PRESSING TO DEAL WITH, HERE, MISTER MOHLMAN.

YOU BEING BROUGHT HERE IS ALL OVER THE NEWS, SUPERMAN, AND THE FACT THAT YOU WERE INJURED -- OR POSSIBLY DEAD --

-- AN EASY TARGET FOR ANYONE LOOKING TO MAKE A NAME FOR THEMSELVES.

THINGS HAVE ESCALATED.

OH, NO.

AAAH!

WHAT IN GOD'S NAME --

IS EVERYONE ALL RIGHT?

YES!

YEAH.

I THINK SO.

GREAT. GLAD TO HEAR IT. NOW, IF YOU COULD ALL -- PLEASE -- MOVE QUICKLY AND CAREFULLY TO SAFETY.

WHOO!

THEY SAID YOU WERE WEAK AND NEAR DEATH. GUESS IT'S TRUE WHAT THEY SAY -- YOU CAN'T TRUST THE MEDIA.

OOOOOH, THIS *ISN'T* MY DAY.

NO. IT'S OURS.

CHOOM

YOUR RELATIONSHIP WITH LOIS HAS *NOTHING* TO DO WITH ME. I *KNOW* THAT.

AND *I* KNOW HOW I FEEL, BUT IT FAILED *ONCE* ALREADY IN SMALLVILLE.

I'M ONLY HERE BECAUSE *SOMEONE* HAD TO BE. SO LET'S LEAVE *ME* OUT OF IT FOR THE MOMENT.

SHE OBVIOUSLY WANTS A BIG, BAD *SUPERMAN* KILLER. NOT SOME LOSER WHO CRIES LIKE A LITTLE GIRL WHEN THINGS GET A TAD HAIRY.

AIN'T LOVE GRAND?

LEARN TO STAND ON YOUR OWN.

GOMORRAH! DON'T LEAVE ME!

SLUMPF

YOU MARRIED SOMEONE WHO WANTED A *SUPERMAN*--

--THE PERFECT ALIEN, THE KNIGHT IN SHINING ARMOR, THE MAN WHO NEVER FAILS -- AND LUCKY FOR YOU, YOU'VE BEEN ABLE TO BE THAT FOR HER.

BUT *NOW* YOU'RE SHOWING WEAKNESS-- FRAILTY--

--HUMANITY--

--AND SHE'S NOT HERE.

COVER
GALLERY

ACTION COMICS #817
Art by Art Adams

ACTION COMICS #819
Art by Art Adams

GOG

Real Name: **William**
(last name unknown)
Occupation: **Fanatic**
Base of Operations: **Mobile**
Height: **6' 3"**
Weight: **210 lbs.**
Eyes: **White**
Hair: **None**
First Appearance: **NEW YEAR'S EVIL: GOG #1** (February, 1998)

Decades into the future, a young boy named William became the lone survivor of a cataclysmic event that resulted in the destruction of Kansas. Rescued by Superman, the boy grew up convinced that he had survived to become the Man of Steel's disciple. But when Superman confessed to him years later that the tragedy was a consequence of his choice to distance himself from mankind's affairs, Willaim was devastated, and suddenly viewed his savior as an "antichrist."

It was at that time when the Quintessence — cosmic immortals including the Phantom Stranger, the New Gods' Highfather, Ganthet of the Guardians, Zeus and the wizard Shazam — bestowed immeasurable power and knowledge upon William, so that he might journey to the past and avert the disaster in Kansas. Instead, he decided to accelerate the event, and thereby publicly expose Superman as the ultimate evil. Armed with a staff powerful enough to rival even the Quintessence's might, William assumed the mantle of Gog and began traveling further and further back in time, murdering Superman countless times along the way. The present-day Man of Steel, aided by Batman, Wonder Woman and their counterparts from an undetermined future, barely thwarted Gog's mission, but his threat has since resurfaced.

Text by **Mike McAver**
Art by **Ivan Reis &
Marc Campos**, with
Dave Stewart

SUPERMAN LIBRARY

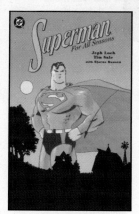

**SUPERMAN
FOR ALL SEASONS**

Jeph Loeb/Tim Sale

**SUPERMAN IN THE FIFTIES
SUPERMAN IN THE SIXIES
SUPERMAN IN THE
SEVENTIES**

various

**BATMAN: HUSH
VOLUMES 1 & 2**

Jeph Loeb/Jim Lee/Scott Williams

SUPERMAN: BIRTHRIGHT

Mark Waid/Leinil Francis Yu/
Gerry Alanguilan

**SUPERMAN: MAN OF STEEL
VOLUMES 1 - 3**

John Byrne/Marv Wolfman/
Jerry Ordway

**SUPERMAN:
UNCONVENTIONAL WARFARE**

Greg Rucka/various

**SUPERMAN:
OUR WORLDS AT WAR
VOLUMES 1 & 2**

various

SUPERMAN: GODFALL

Michael Turner/Joe Kelly/Talent Caldwell/
Jason Gorder/Peter Steigerwald

DEATH OF SUPERMAN

various

RETURN OF SUPERMAN

various

**SUPERMAN/BATMAN:
PUBLIC ENEMIES**

Jeph Loeb/Ed McGuinness/
Dexter Vines

**SUPERMAN:
THE GREATEST STORIES
EVER TOLD!**

various